THE STORY OF THE PROPHET YUSUF عليه السلام

SANIYASNAIN   KHAN

A small token
of Love

For
Sweet Ayesha

From
Zareen Khala
Dhaka
23/ 01/ 02

Goodword
FOR KIDS

نَحْنُ نَقُصُّ عَلَيْكَ أَحْسَنَ الْقَصَصِ
بِمَا أَوْحَيْنَا إِلَيْكَ هٰذَا الْقُرْآنَ
وَإِن كُنتَ مِن قَبْلِهِ لَمِنَ الْغَفِلِينَ

In revealing this Quran
We will recount to you the most
beautiful of stories, though
before it you were heedless.
(12:3)

First published in 2001
© Goodword Books 2001

GOODWORD BOOKS
1, Nizamuddin West Market,
New Delhi 110 013
Tel. 435 5454, 435 1128, 435 6666
Fax 9111-435 7333, 435 7980
E-mail: skhan@vsnl.com
www.goodwordforkids.com

Illustrations by
K.M. Ravindran

THE STORY OF THE PROPHET YUSUF علیه السلام

*L*ong, long ago in a far-away place in Canaan, near Nablus, some thirty miles north of Jerusalem, lived a pious old man. His name was Ya'qub علیه السلام. He and his family and other relatives lived in tents woven from goat hair, and sent their animals to graze in the nearby hills and valleys. These were very fertile places and had little groves of trees dotted here and there all over them.

The pasture-land was so rich that they could stay for a long time in one place and did not have to move every week or so as some tribes did. Usually, they spent their time looking after their herds of animals, milking their goats and sheep and making household things. Everything they did was to help and support their large family. They would also load their pack animals with animal skins and meat and whatever cloth they had woven, and would go to distant places to sell them. Sometimes they went out into the hills and hunted.

Yaqub عليه السلام was the grandson of the great Prophet Ibrahim عليه السلام. He himself was a prophet, and also the leader of the whole tribe. He had twelve sons, Yusuf عليه السلام being the second youngest of them. As a baby, Yusuf عليه السلام spent his time in and around the family, playing with the other children, enjoying himself with the animals and looking out to the vast desert lands. His father loved him dearly. From the very beginning his father was very impressed by this young, noble, gentle soul, for whom he saw a great and promising future. Yusuf عليه السلام had ten elder half brothers from another mother. His real brother, who was younger than he, was called Binyamin.

One day Yusuf عليه السلام, who was a boy of keen intelligence and a kind nature, had an unusual dream, in which eleven stars and the sun and the moon all bowed down to him. When he woke up, he hurried to tell his father about this strange dream. Yaqub ﷺ understood right away that great things lay in store for his young and best-loved son. This had been made plain in the dream. Sensing that Yusuf's half brothers might become jealous of him and try to harm him, he warned him not to tell them about it: "My little son, do not tell your brothers about your dream lest they hatch a plot against you, for Satan is the open enemy of man." He told him to be careful, saying, "The Lord has chosen you, Yusuf, for a higher purpose. He will teach you to interpret dreams, and will perfect His blessings upon you." Then he said that Allah would bless him and their family in just the way He had blessed his grandfather Ishaq ﷺ and his great grandfather Ibrahim ﷺ.

In the meantime, being aware of their father's great love for Yusuf ﷺ, the ten half-brothers became so resentful that they began to hate him. They would say, "Surely, our father is clearly wrong." They would go off, grumbling and muttering, to look after the family's flocks. They became so jealous of their father's special love for Yusuf ﷺ that they banded together and plotted against him. The young Yusuf ﷺ was innocent and did not even know of his brothers' guile and hatred, but his father knew and warned him. The ten brothers not only hated their innocent younger half-brothers, Yusuf ﷺ and Binyamin, but they

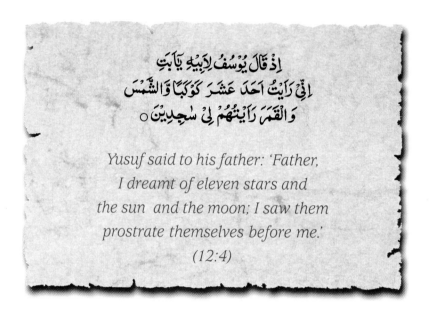

Yusuf said to his father: 'Father,
I dreamt of eleven stars and
the sun and the moon; I saw them
prostrate themselves before me.'
(12:4)

showed disrespect to their noble father by treating him as an ignorant old fool.

In fact, Yaqub ﷺ, his father Ishaq and grandfather Ibrahim, all being prophets, had been commanded by Allah to pass on their knowledge to the tribe and to the family. Some took heed of what they said and some did not, but the family as a whole benefited from having such forebears. But when Yaqub ﷺ tried to teach his own older sons anything, they paid no heed to his words of wisdom.

Finally the ten brothers became so resentful that they went off to the hills to hatch a plot where nobody could hear or see them. There they suggested something really outrageous. They said to each other: "Yusuf and his younger brother are dearer to our father than we are, though we are so many. Truly, our father is very much mistaken. Let us slay Yusuf, or cast him away in some far-off land, so that we have no rivals for our father's love, and after that be honourable men." As with evil in their hearts they debated how to rid themselves of Yusuf عليه السلام, one of the brothers objected to killing him, for he was somewhat sympathetic towards him. He suggested, "Do not slay Yusuf, but, if you must, throw him rather into a dark well. Some caravan will pull him out."

They all liked this idea and agreed upon it. And

they knew where just such a well was to be found. It was deep and had completely dried up.

But now, for their plot to succeed, they had to deceive their father. So one day, they made a plan to go on a supposed hunting trip outside the village and all of them came to their father and pretended to be very sincere:

"Dear Father! Why don't you trust us with Yusuf? We certainly wish him well. Send him with us tomorrow, so that he can play and enjoy himself."

They assured their father that they would take good care of him. But Yaqub ؏ sensed a plot, and was unwilling to agree, lest some harm befall his favourite son. "I would feel very anxious if I let him go with you," said Yaqub, "in case some wolf came along and ate him up while you were off your guard." But the brothers kept on persuading him: "It would be shameful if the wolf devoured him while there are so many of us." They made Yaqub ؏ believe that the ten strong, grown-up men would have to die before the wolf could touch the young Yusuf! So they had their way, for finally Yaqub ؏ relented and put aside his fear, although he felt unhappy about the whole idea. What Yaqub ؏ did not know was that the brothers were planning, out of envy, to rid themselves of Yusuf ﷺ. In saying he feared that a wolf might come and attack Yusuf ﷺ, he really unwittingly gave the wicked ones an idea. Thus the evil plot thickened.

The next morning, as Yaqub ﷺ saw his children off, he prayed for the safety and well-being, of all of them, especially his beloved son Yusuf ﷺ, who was about 16 years old at that time. Yaqub ﷺ was a prophet with incredible patience. He believed that Allah would always be with his children and would help them in times of need, although he did not know in what form Allah's help would come.

They went deep into the countryside, taking their sheep and goats with them to let them graze on the hillsides. Yusuf ﷺ was very cheerful and excited to be out on a trip with his elder brothers. He ran happily here and there with great joy and excitement and played among them contentedly.

But hardly had his brothers taken leave of their father back in their settlement than they decided it was time to put their terrible plan into action. Coming close to the well, they took Yusuf ﷺ unawares, seizing him from behind and grasping him by the arms and legs. He fought so hard to free himself that his shirt was dragged off his back. But no matter how he struggled, he was unable to escape their clutches, for they were so much bigger than he was. They dragged him to the nearby well and threw him down into it. He screamed as he fell, but they paid no heed.

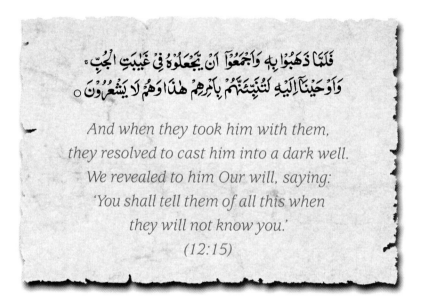

فَلَمَّا ذَهَبُوا بِهِ وَأَجْمَعُوٓا أَن يَجْعَلُوهُ فِى غَيَبَتِ الْجُبِّ ۚ وَأَوْحَيْنَآ إِلَيْهِ لَتُنَبِّئَنَّهُم بِأَمْرِهِمْ هَٰذَا وَهُمْ لَا يَشْعُرُونَ ۝

And when they took him with them,
they resolved to cast him into a dark well.
We revealed to him Our will, saying:
'You shall tell them of all this when
they will not know you.'
(12:15)

Although the well was quite deep, it had completely dried up. Yusuf ﷺ landed on the dry bottom of the well with a thud. He was shaken by the fall, but had no injuries except for some cuts made by the sharp edges of some stones on the inside of the well.

There would be no climbing those steep slippery sides to escape. The brothers had run away, laughing and joking after committing such an evil deed and had paid no attention to Yusuf's desperate cries for help. Left there without food or water, he lay there all alone for three days. He turned towards his Lord in the hopes of receiving His help. Then Allah revealed His will to him, saying : "You shall tell them of all this when they will not know you." Yusuf's future was probably shown in a dream that he would come out of the well and that, some day, he would be so much higher in rank that,

11

when his brothers saw him, they would not even recognise him. And perhaps one day they would stand in need of him, and he would be in a position to help them. This would put them to shame for their present plotting and betrayal. And so one day he would be the master of his present enemies.

Allah was with Yusuf ﷺ, in all his difficulties, sorrows and sufferings, as He is with all His servants who put their trust in Him. Yusuf ﷺ may have been betrayed by his brothers, and left to die or be sold into slavery, but he was undaunted. His courage never failed him.

But the evil brothers were busy now making another plan—this time to fool their own father. They killed a young goat and smeared Yusuf's shirt with its blood.

They waited until nightfall, before going back home to show that they had made an effort to search for their brother and save him. They pretended to be crying. "O father!" they wept, "What you feared has actually happened! We ran races and left Yusuf to look after our belongings. No sooner had we turned our backs than a wolf, seeing that Yusuf was alone, attacked him and ate him up." They produced his shirt soaked with the goat's blood as evidence.

The Prophet Yaqub's fear about the wolf made them imagine that he would readily believe this story.

Yaqub ﷺ was very distressed and utterly shocked to hear this terrible news. He heard the story about the wolf, but did not believe it. He was a wise man and could read their hearts. He saw that there had been some foul play. When he examined the shirt, he saw that it was certainly blood-stained, but was not torn anywhere. So in his heart he refused to accept the story: "If the wolf had eaten him, it would have torn his shirt as well!" In other words, how gentle the wolf must have been to devour Yusuf ﷺ but leave the shirt untouched! "No!" he cried, "Your souls have tempted you to evil. Sweet patience! *(sabr jamil)*! Allah alone can help me to bear the loss." Thus Yaqub ﷺ stilled his heart and begged Allah's assistance.

For days, Yaqub ﷺ did not speak.

The brothers thought that their father would love them better now that Yusuf ﷺ was out of the way, but this was not so. All Yaqub ﷺ did was spend more time in prayer and meditation. He asked Allah's protection for his little son. He would console himself by remembering Yusuf's dream of eleven stars and the sun and the moon. He was confident that Yusuf ﷺ must be alive somewhere and that Allah had very likely chosen him for some more noble destiny.

While his dear father sorrowed for him, Yusuf ﷺ lay at the bottom of the dark well, feeling terrified because there was no way to get out. But, in the meantime, a

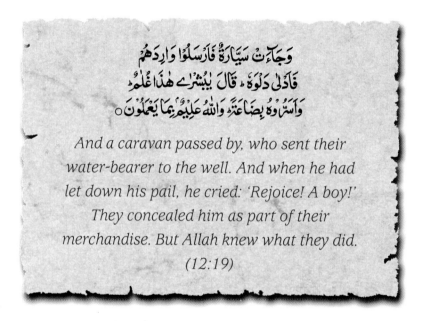

وَجَآءَتْ سَيَّارَةٌ فَأَرْسَلُوْا وَارِدَهُمْ
فَأَدْلَىٰ دَلْوَهُ ۙ قَالَ يٰبُشْرٰى هٰذَا غُلٰمٌ
وَأَسَرُّوْهُ بِضَاعَةً ۚ وَاللهُ عَلِيْمٌۢ بِمَا يَعْمَلُوْنَ ۞

And a caravan passed by, who sent their water-bearer to the well. And when he had let down his pail, he cried: 'Rejoice! A boy!' They concealed him as part of their merchandise. But Allah knew what they did.
(12:19)

caravan bound for Egypt was coming down from Syria and travelling through Palestine. It had come from the east of the Jordan river, from Gilead (Gilead is the ancient name for the region east of the Jordan), and kept close to the coast. In those days, people mostly bartered their goods, rather than use money. So they had to carry a lot of things and these had to be well-guarded. This caravan was carrying dried fruits, spices, medicine, balm and incense, etc. It also carried cloth, pots, and a few other things. All of these were packed in the saddle-bags carried by camels, whose broad feet spread comfortably on the sandy tracks.

Although the camels' movements were silent, there was a constant tinkling sound of their halter bells. There were also the long, low calls, made by the camel-drivers, one by one, as they moved at an even pace along the well-known track. They were expecting to reach the next well very soon, and when they did, a water carrier was sent off to draw some water for the animals and the travellers.

Suddenly, the water-carrier cried out : "Oh, good news! Here's a lucky find! A boy at the bottom of the well!"

Everyone ran to the well and were puzzled to see Yusuf ﷺ at the bottom, trying his hardest to climb out. They threw down a rope, which he tied around his waist and they hauled him up. Imagine the travellers' surprise when they saw a good-looking boy coming out of the well with a face as bright as the sun! He looked as innocent as an angel, and had a very fine appearance.

Instead of sending the child home after rescuing him, they decided to take him with them to Egypt where they would sell him at the slave market.

The caravan, with its softly padding camels, travelled down the coast, along the outer rim of the Sinai Desert and across the narrow stretch of land between the Red

Sea and the Mediterranean. Their journey would soon be over, when they reached Egypt.

The Nile, flowing all the way from Ethiopia which is much further south, passes through Sudan before entering the broad valley in Egypt which takes its name from the river.

Once a year the river used to overflow its banks. This was terrible for the people, because their houses and lands would often disappear beneath the waters. Even worse, the river changed its course every year, when the waters were reaching their highest level. But the good part about the flood waters was that they carried all sorts of earth and sand from further south, and, deposited it on the land. This living matter, called silt, is a natural fertiliser which makes crops flourish. It was this, along with the waters of the Nile, which had made Egypt one of the richest lands in the region for thousands of years. As a result, the Egyptians had a mighty empire with powerful kings, some of whom were later known as Pharaohs or Firawns.

When the caravan arrived, probably in the ancient city of Memphis in Egypt, Yusuf عليه السلام was sold for the paltry sum of 20 dirhams (small silver coins), to a nobleman, who took him into his service. This was Allah's plan to save Yusuf عليه السلام and give him an honourable position. The man who bought Yusuf عليه السلام was from the royal court and bore the title of Aziz (a title which was given to people of high rank, such as governors. His name was Fitfir, or Potiphar). The Aziz could tell that there was something very special about this young man. Yusuf's handsome

وَقَالَ الَّذِى اشْتَرَاهُ مِنْ مِّصْرَ لِامْرَاَتِهٖٓ اَكْرِمِىْ
مَثْوَاهُ عَسٰىٓ اَنْ يَّنْفَعَنَآ اَوْ نَتَّخِذَهٗ وَلَدًا ۚ وَكَذٰلِكَ مَكَّنَّا لِيُوْسُفَ
فِى الْاَرْضِ ۖ وَلِنُعَلِّمَهٗ مِنْ تَاْوِيْلِ الْاَحَادِيْثِ ۚ وَاللّٰهُ غَالِبٌ عَلٰٓى اَمْرِهٖ
وَلٰكِنَّ اَكْثَرَ النَّاسِ لَا يَعْلَمُوْنَ ۝

The Egyptian who bought him said to his wife:
'Be kind to him. He may prove useful to us, or
we may adopt him as our son.' Thus We
established Yusuf in the land, and taught him
to interpret dreams. Allah has power over all
things, though most men may not know it.
(12:21)

presence, his good nature, his winning ways, his purity and innocence, his intelligence and integrity, combined with his courtesy and noble manliness, greatly attracted the Aziz to him. Sensing that this handsome boy must be from a noble family, this Egyptian nobleman did not regard Yusuf عليه السلام as a slave.

So he brought him home and instructed his wife to take good care of him. He asked her to treat him as an honoured member of the household, adding that, as they had no children, they might later on adopt him as a son.

Thus, according to Allah's plan, Yusuf عليه السلام was brought from a small village to the most advanced city of the

age to be trained and to do some purposeful task. Whenever some hardship befalls believers—it is very likely that Allah is planning something better for them, as in the case of Yusuf ﷺ: he was thrown into a well only to be taken to a better place. But this happens only if the people concerned endure their misfortunes with patience.

Thus Yusuf ﷺ was brought up in a noble family of very high rank and given excellent training and education. He turned into a man of remarkable ability and wisdom.

The years passed and Yusuf ﷺ grew into a young man of remarkable beauty and charm. With his change of fortune in Egypt, he grew in knowledge, judgement and power. The Aziz had treated Yusuf ﷺ with honour: he was more his guest and son than his slave. He had quickly learnt the language and had become almost like an Egyptian. He himself was truthful and honest, so people would ask his advice and respect his opinions.

The Aziz's wife, whose name was Zulaykha, felt very attracted to Yusuf ﷺ, but he kept his distance and never responded to her advances. She would not take no for an answer, and followed Yusuf ﷺ around. But Yusuf ﷺ would not listen to her. One day when the Aziz was away, his wife, finding Yusuf ﷺ on his own, called him into her room and tried to seduce him. She bolted the doors and said: "Come!" The temptation was so strong that, if he had not been strengthened by his great faith in Allah, he would have fallen a prey to mortal weakness. Taken aback, Yusuf ﷺ said, "God forbid. My master has treated me with kindness. I cannot betray his trust." He felt that the Aziz, who had not only been kind to him, but had treated him with courtesy and honour, was entitled to more than mere gratitude from him. Moreover, Yusuf ﷺ knew that it would be a sin against Allah. Therefore, Yusuf ﷺ took to his heels and ran towards the door. She also ran after him and caught hold of his shirt and tore it from behind. Yusuf ﷺ managed to open the door, only to find his master standing outside. The Aziz's wife was very quick-witted. She had to resort to a lie not only to justify herself, but also to have her revenge on the man who had scorned her. She cleverly thought of a way out by trying to put the blame on Yusuf ﷺ: "What is the fitting punishment, my master, for one who has evil designs on your wife?" she cried. A moment before she had been showing her love for him, and now she began to accuse him falsely of misbehaving with her. Yusuf ﷺ denied her charges and explained that it was she who had tried to seduce him. By this time a number of family members had gathered there to find out what the commotion was about. A member of the household who had probably seen everything suggested, "If Yusuf's

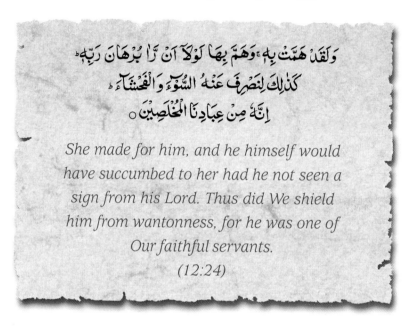

وَلَقَدْ هَمَّتْ بِهِ ۖ وَهَمَّ بِهَا لَوْلَا أَن رَّأَىٰ بُرْهَانَ رَبِّهِ ۚ كَذَٰلِكَ لِنَصْرِفَ عَنْهُ السُّوءَ وَالْفَحْشَاءَ ۚ إِنَّهُ مِنْ عِبَادِنَا الْمُخْلَصِينَ ۝

She made for him, and he himself would have succumbed to her had he not seen a sign from his Lord. Thus did We shield him from wantonness, for he was one of Our faithful servants.

(12:24)

shirt is torn from the front, she is speaking the truth. If it is torn from behind, then it is he who is to be believed." When her husband saw that Yusuf's shirt was really torn from behind, he realized his wife's fault, and exclaimed: "Your cunning is great indeed!" Then he scolded her and ordered her to ask Yusuf's pardon.

Yusuf ﷺ kept intact his divine nature, which saved him at this delicate moment. Every single human being is gifted with this divine nature right from his or her birth. This helps him to judge between right and wrong and to tell the difference between good and evil. Such a nature cautions him on all occasions. One who ignores this, ignores the gentle voice of God. Such a person will not only be deprived of Allah's help, but will slowly weaken this inherent nature. On the other hand, one who is obedient to his Creator will bow the moment Allah's call is heard. Allah's help gives such a person the strength to resist any such evil.

The news of the incident spread throughout the town and the womenfolk in particular began to gossip about it. Then the Aziz's wife invited the noble ladies of the town to a banquet. Giving each of them a knife, she told them to cut some fruit. Then she asked Yusuf عليه السلام to pass through the dining room. When Yusuf عليه السلام appeared, the ladies were so struck by his extraordinary good looks that they exclaimed: "God preserve us! This is no mortal but a gracious angel!" And, in great excitement, they cut their fingers with the knives in their hands.

The women may have been greatly taken with the attractive personality of Yusuf عليه السلام but, Yusuf عليه السلام, on the contrary, had his entire attention focussed on Allah. He was so absorbed in the greatness and sublimity of Allah that no other thing was able to attract him.

The Aziz's wife did not change her attitude towards Yusuf عليه السلام. She even threatened to send him to prison. Thus Yusuf عليه السلام prayed in great anguish, "Help me, O my Lord; prison will be better than what I am being asked to do. If you do not save me from their plot, I will incline towards them, and then I will be one of the ignorant people."

Even though the Aziz and others knew that Yusuf ﷺ was innocent, they decided, probably on his wife's insistence, to imprison him. That was unjust, but it was also Allah's answer to his prayer. Prison opens another chapter in the life of the Prophet Yusuf ﷺ. Allah always plans things which are for the betterment of the believer; even if at face value they look like hardships, they may eventually turn out to be blessings. This is exactly what happened in the case of the Prophet Yusuf ﷺ. Allah rewards those who preserve their chastity and are patient about what befalls them. Therefore, Allah was with Yusuf ﷺ. He had not forgotten him. He had a great plan for his future.

No sunlight entered the prison. It was so dark that one could not tell whether it was day or night. And it was so locked and bared that there could be no escape from it. But Yusuf ﷺ kept on praying to his Lord. He remembered how Allah had rescued him from the dark well. He was sure that Allah would help him once again.

Yusuf ﷺ was innocent. He had a clear conscience. As such, he was no ordinary prisoner and waited patiently for Allah to reprieve him. In the meantime, he saw his being locked up in prison as a good thing, for it prevented him from falling a prey to the temptation of his master's home. There was, however, another and more important side to his being in prison. It was while he was there that Allah called upon him to become a prophet. In this, he would be following in the footsteps of his father Yaqub ﷺ, his grandfather Ishaq ﷺ and the

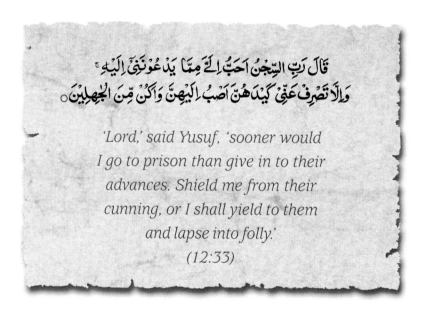

قَالَ رَبِّ السِّجْنُ أَحَبُّ إِلَيَّ مِمَّا يَدْعُونَنِيٓ إِلَيْهِ ۖ
وَإِلَّا تَصْرِفْ عَنِّي كَيْدَهُنَّ أَصْبُ إِلَيْهِنَّ وَأَكُن مِّنَ الْجَٰهِلِينَ

*'Lord,' said Yusuf, 'sooner would
I go to prison than give in to their
advances. Shield me from their
cunning, or I shall yield to them
and lapse into folly.'*
(12:33)

his great grandfather Ibrahim ﷺ. And so it was that while he was still in prison, Yusuf ﷺ began his mission by bringing the word of Allah to the other inmates. He begged criminals to change their ways and sympathized with those who had been wrongly convicted. He advised them to put up with their suffering as patiently as they were able.

There were two prisoners who entered the prison at the same time as Yusuf ﷺ. Both were servants in the royal court, who had displeased the king. One of them was the king's cup-bearer. His job was to serve wine to the king. The other one was the king's baker. Each had been charged with conspiring to poison the king. They were both impressed by the Prophet Yusuf's honesty and wisdom. They trusted him and used to consult him.

One night each of them had a strange dream. They came to Yusuf ﷺ, told him of their dreams and requested him to interpret them.

One told him that he saw himself pressing grapes to make wine. The other said that in his dream he saw himself carrying some bread on his head which was pecked at by birds.

After recounting these details, they requested Yusuf ﷺ, to tell them their meaning, for they could see he was a man of virtue. Yusuf ﷺ replied that they would learn everything before their next meal. He added that this ability to interpret dreams had been given to him by his Lord.

He felt that it was the right time to teach them the true faith. So he taught them to believe in one true God and told them to give up their old, evil ways of idol-worshipping :

Fellow prisoners! Are several Lords better, or Allah the One, the Almighty? Those you worship besides Him are nothing but names which you and your fathers have devised and for which Allah has revealed no sanction. Judgement rests only with Allah. He has commanded you to worship none but Him. That is the true faith: yet most men do not know it. (12:39-40)

After teaching them the faith, Yusuf ﷺ interpreted

the dreams which they saw. To the first, Yusuf ﷺ said that he would shortly be released from the prison and would pour wine for his master. To the other he said that he would be sentenced to death and birds would peck at his head. Yusuf ﷺ asked the one who would serve wine in the royal court to be sure to mention to the king how cruelly he had been thrown into prison, although he was completely innocent.

Not long after, the Prophet Yusuf's prediction came true. After being put on trial, one of the prisoners—the baker—was found guilty and charged with trying to poison the king. Thus the baker was condemned to death.

However, the charges against the cup-bearer having been proved false, he was released and returned to the palace to his old job of serving wine to the king. But the cup-bearer completely forgot the Prophet Yusuf's request to mention to the king that he had been wronged and was awaiting his release. Therefore, Yusuf ﷺ was left to languish in the prison for several more years.

In the meanwhile, one night the king of Egypt had a very strange dream which he failed to understand. He called his advisors, courtiers and priests to interpret the dream for him. All the learned men of the land came to the king, who told of how in his dream he had seen seven weak cows devouring seven fat ones, and seven green ears of corn being replaced by seven dry ones.

The king asked them to explain the meaning of these events. Everyone gave some answer and tried his best to throw light on the dream, but none of them gave an

يٰصَاحِبَيِ السِّجْنِ
ءَاَرْبَابٌ مُّتَفَرِّقُوْنَ خَيْرٌ
اَمِ اللّٰهُ الْوَاحِدُ الْقَهَّارُ ﴿

'Fellow prisoners!
Are sundry gods better than Allah,
the One who conquers all?
(12:39)

answer which could satisfy the king. He was very disappointed by the interpretation of all the wise men of Egypt and desperately wanted to find someone who could do better. At this moment the cup-bearer, who had been imprisoned some years back and had met Yusuf عليه السلام in the prison, remembered him and his great ability to interpret dreams. He told the king about Yusuf عليه السلام and how the interpretation which Yusuf ﷺ gave to their dreams had come true down to the very last detail. The king was very happy at this and sent the cup-bearer to the prison to meet Yusuf ﷺ.

In the prison, he requested Yusuf ﷺ to explain this dream, which had baffled all the others: "Tell us, O truthful one, of the seven fat cows which seven weak ones devoured; also of the seven green ears of corn and the

other seven which were dry."

Yusuf ﷺ then interpreted the king's dream. He explained that in the lands of Egypt there would be seven years of prosperity. They would grow lots of grain and the cattle would greatly multiply. But following these seven years of prosperity and abundance, there would come seven years of severe and dreadful famine, when crops would not grow, cattle would die and people would starve to death. These seven years would use up all the stores which they had laid by in the good years. He also offered him a solution to this problem. He said that, in the first seven years, whatever crops were grown should be mostly saved. In this way, during the years of famine they would be able to use the grain which had been stored, so that facing the famine would be much less difficult. He also foretold that after seven years of famine, there would come a year when there would be abundant rain and they would be blessed with great prosperity. In that year the vines and the olive trees which had suffered in the drought, would be revived and would yield their juice and they would have the oil from the linseed, sesame and the caster oil plant, etc.

When the cup-bearer made Yusuf's interpretation known to the king he realized that Yusuf ﷺ was gifted with great knowledge, and was very pleased. Wanting to meet him in person, he ordered that Yusuf ﷺ be brought into his presence.

When the king's messenger arrived at the prison to fetch Yusuf ﷺ to the royal palace, he expected that the prisoner would be overjoyed at the king's summons. But to his amazement, Yusuf ﷺ refused to leave the prison until his name was cleared. Yusuf ﷺ was to carry out the prophetic mission of Allah. For this important duty, it was very necessary that any false charges should be cleared and he should emerge with a clean image.

The king ordered an enquiry into the Prophet Yusuf's complaint and found that all the charges against him had been falsely made up. The Aziz's wife and other women were called by the king and he asked them, "What made you attempt to seduce Yusuf?" The Aziz's wife openly admitted her crime saying: "We know no evil of him." "Now the truth must come to light," she said, "It was I who attempted to seduce him. He has told the truth."

When Yusuf ﷺ learned about the confession made by the Aziz's wife, he thanked Allah from depth of his heart and exclaimed: "Now my former master (the Aziz) will know that I did not betray him behind his back, and that Allah does not guide those who betray their trust." Then he added: "I am not trying to absolve myself: for man's inner self does tempt him to do evil, and only those

وَقَالَ الْمَلِكُ إِنِّيٓ أَرَىٰ سَبْعَ بَقَرَٰتٍ سِمَانٍ يَأْكُلُهُنَّ سَبْعٌ عِجَافٌ وَسَبْعَ سُنۢبُلَٰتٍ خُضْرٍ وَأُخَرَ يَابِسَٰتٍ ۖ يَٰٓأَيُّهَا الْمَلَأُ أَفْتُونِى فِى رُءْيَٰىَ إِن كُنتُمْ لِلرُّءْيَا تَعْبُرُونَ ۝

The king said: 'I saw seven fat cows which seven lean ones devoured; also seven green ears of corn and seven others dry. Tell me the meaning of this dream, my nobles, if you can interpret dreams.

(12:43)

are saved upon whom my Lord bestows His mercy. My Lord is forgiving and merciful."

The Prophet Yusuf ﷺ did not say that his victory was his own, but pointed out that it was solely thanks to the grace and mercy of Allah.

Thus Yusuf ﷺ was honourably released from the prison. When he appeared before the king, the latter was very impressed by his extraordinary personality and especially when his innocence, wisdom, truthfulness and trustworthiness had been proved beyond any shadow of a doubt. The king honoured Yusuf ﷺ by making him his most trusted minister. The king said to him, "From now on you shall dwell with us, honoured and trusted." Yusuf ﷺ said, "Give me charge of the granaries of the realm. I shall be a good and intelligent keeper." With this promise Yusuf ﷺ said he would organize the storage of food for the years of famine. Because the king felt Yusuf ﷺ was the person most capable of dealing with the coming crisis,

he happily made him the minister of granaries and charged him with providing enough grain to meet all needs during the famine which would strike Egypt seven years later. The Prophet Yusuf عليه السلام was about 30 years old when he received this appointment.

Thus Allah established Yusuf عليه السلام securely in the lands of Egypt. Sometimes it is the hardships in life that lead the way to better times. In the case of the Prophet Yusuf عليه السلام, when he was thrown into the dark well, it was apparently a great hardship for him. But the world is managed and governed by Allah alone, and He makes special plans for His servants. So the well became the first step for Yusuf عليه السلام to reach great heights, taken as he was from a small village to the most modern city of that time in Egypt and ultimately finding an honourable position in the house of a noble prince. Likewise the dark prison became a stepping stone to the royal court and ultimately to the seat of power in the lands of Egypt.

Misfortune and failure in life are common occurrences, but coupled with a positive attitude, they can be turned into success. Failure, on the other hand, coupled with a negative attitude remains a failure. There is no end to the possibilities of success in life for the individual who can take a lesson from failure. But life's trials must be faced with patience, perseverance and compassion.

The story of the Prophet Yusuf ﷺ is a great reminder to believers to put their entire trust in Allah and to pray to Him in good times, as well as in adversity. As the Quran puts it: "Every hardship comes with ease." (94:5-6).

Yusuf ﷺ set about his important duties. He travelled the length and breadth of Egypt. In every city he gave orders for huge storage buildings to be put up, to hold grain. Accordingly, large granaries were erected and grain was stored in them bit by bit. Together with the farmers and land owners he collected as much grain as possible. Seven years of wonderful harvests brought in huge quantities of grain.

Yusuf ﷺ arranged for it to be stored all over the country. Before the seven years were up, the new store houses were completely full, so that the frightening seven years of famine could be taken care of.

As second in command to the king, and with the blessings of Almighty Allah, Yusuf ﷺ swept throughout the lands of Egypt, where everyone bowed to his authority and his wisdom. Recognizing his power and his talent for organization, people in all of Egypt's cities, were glad to do as they were bade. For seven whole years, they amassed their plentiful harvests. There was grain without measure, piling up until it was like the sands of the desert. It was loaded on to carts to be dispatched to places where it was most needed and also sent down the river by

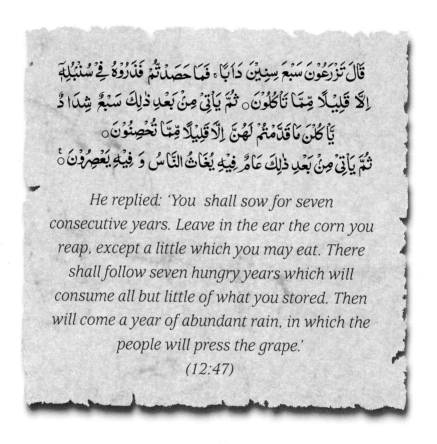

قَالَ تَزْرَعُوْنَ سَبْعَ سِنِيْنَ دَاَبًا ۚ فَمَا حَصَدْتُّمْ فَذَرُوْهُ فِيْ سُنْبُلِهٖٓ
اِلَّا قَلِيْلًا مِّمَّا تَاْكُلُوْنَ ۞ ثُمَّ يَاْتِيْ مِنْ بَعْدِ ذٰلِكَ سَبْعٌ شِدَادٌ
يَّاْكُلْنَ مَا قَدَّمْتُمْ لَهُنَّ اِلَّا قَلِيْلًا مِّمَّا تُحْصِنُوْنَ ۞
ثُمَّ يَاْتِيْ مِنْۢ بَعْدِ ذٰلِكَ عَامٌ فِيْهِ يُغَاثُ النَّاسُ وَ فِيْهِ يَعْصِرُوْنَ ۞

He replied: 'You shall sow for seven consecutive years. Leave in the ear the corn you reap, except a little which you may eat. There shall follow seven hungry years which will consume all but little of what you stored. Then will come a year of abundant rain, in which the people will press the grape.'

(12:47)

barges from the great Nile delta. The granaries were gradually filling up, for Yusuf عليه السلام had managed everything with superb skill. During the seven good years, he saw to it that there was enough grain to see them through the hard times that were coming. He had successfully completed his preparations.

The seven good years passed and the times of prosperity ended. Then came the seven lean and hungry years, when no crops would grow. Now, famine held the land in its grip. The whole of Egypt was hit by it. The

skies became white and hot and stayed that way; never a drop of water did they let fall upon the land. The land cracked, and the dry wind whipped up storms of dust. The Nile river shrivelled, and people began to starve and animals began to die. Famine was everywhere.

Now, Yusuf ﷿ was busier than ever, distributing and selling the grain that had been saved and seeing that it was fairly shared out.

For when the famine started, it affected many of Egypt's near and distant neighbours too. Many countries on the shores of the Mediterranean looked to Egypt as a source of food. Caravans came from all directions—from Syria and Arabia and the coast of North Africa—all hoping to buy or barter for grain. Yusuf ﷿ had foreseen these countries' needs and had set aside enough foodstuffs for the purpose. He happily gave grain to everyone who came to him from neighbouring lands. But he restricted each trader to just one camel-load. That was as much as could fairly be given.

Back in the lands of Canaan, Yaqub ﷿ and his sons were hit by the famine too. Like everywhere else, food had become scarce in their land too. When he came to know that people were travelling to Egypt for grain, Yaqub ﷺ asked his sons to go there to fetch some grain for the family, as there was hardly anything to eat. So the brothers saddled their mounts, and set out. Only Binyamin did not accompany them, for Yaqub ﷺ could not endure being separated from him. He was very anxious about him—the only real brother of Yusuf ﷺ.

The ten selfish brothers loaded their camels and began their slow journey towards Egypt. After their long tiring trek, all the ten brothers finally came to the lands of Egypt. Reaching the royal store house to buy grain, they presented themselves to the chief of the store houses, the minister of Egypt's king. Little did they know, when they came to seek provisions from him, that the minister was their own brother, Yusuf ﷺ, whom they had thrown into a dry well, and whom they had presumed to be dead long long ago. It was about 20 years since they had seen him. As soon as the brothers entered the palace, Yusuf ﷺ recognised them. They—not surprisingly—did not recognize him, for it never occurred to them that the young boy whom they had thrown down a dry well, could not only have survived, but have also risen to such a high rank.

Yusuf ﷺ received them courteously but he did not tell them who he really was.

In the course of conversation with them, Yusuf ﷵ asked about their situation and about the number of people in their family. They told him that they had old parents and one younger brother.

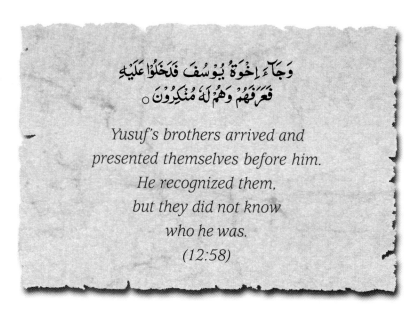

وَجَآءَ إِخْوَةُ يُوسُفَ فَدَخَلُوا عَلَيْهِ فَعَرَفَهُمْ وَهُمْ لَهُ مُنْكِرُونَ ٥

Yusuf's brothers arrived and
presented themselves before him.
He recognized them,
but they did not know
who he was.
(12:58)

Yusuf ﷵ gave them all enough provisions and treated them liberally—one camel load for each one of them. Seeing this, the brothers requested Yusuf ﷵ to give them one more camel load for the brother who had not come with them. Yusuf ﷵ said that they could only provide for those

who were present: "Next time, come with your brother. You have seen my generosity." There was probably some argument and Yusuf ﷺ said forcefully that if they did not bring their brother, they might be thought to be lying. He further threatened them that no grain would be given to them in future if they failed to bring the brother whom they had mentioned. The brothers said, "We will do our very best to persuade our father to part with him." In this way, Yusuf ﷺ thought he would be able to meet his younger brother, Binyamin, whom he very much longed to see.

When they were preparing to leave, Yusuf ﷺ had their money and merchandise put back into their packs.

The happy band of ten brothers left Egypt with enough provisions for the entire year. When they got back home, they opened up their packs and found that their money and merchandise had been returned to them. They were thrilled with the kindness and generosity which the king's minister had shown them. Their opinion of the keeper of the store-houses now rose even higher.

They said to their father, "Oh father! What more could we ask for? All our goods and money have been returned to us! If you will just send Binyamin with us, we shall again be able to bring food for our family. We promise to guard our brother well." But Yaqub ﷺ was very reluctant. It was impossible for him to lose one more son after losing his beloved child Yusuf ﷺ. Though many years had passed, the memory of his loss was still fresh in his mind.

When the time came for them to return to Egypt to obtain grain for the following year, they remembered the words of the king's minister, who had told them to bring Binyamin, so that they could be given more provisions. So they all came to their old father. "Oh father!" they pleaded, "Unless we take Binyamin with us, none of Egypt's grain will be given to us." The father feared for his son, remembering what had happened to Yusuf ﷺ. He asked: "Shall I entrust him to you as I entrusted his brother?"

But they went on and on pleading with him. Their persistence and the urgent need for food, finally made Yaqub ﷺ agree to send his youngest son with his ten half-brothers. But before that, he took from every one of them a solemn promise before Allah, that they would indeed take good care of him and bring him back home safely, unless they themselves were ambushed. They all promised. It was a serious moment, and everyone pledged his life to protect Binyamin. Yaqub ﷺ said, "Allah is witness to all that we say."

Then the Prophet Yaqub ﷺ advised his sons: "My sons, do not all enter the city by one gate. Enter it by different gates." He probably gave this advice in case the local people, seeing so many outsiders entering the city, tried to stop them. Then he cautioned them: "In no way can I shield you from the might of Allah. Judgement is His alone."

In other words, though he gave worldly advice to his sons to enter the city in small groups, at the same time he showed his utmost trust in Allah, saying that whatever happened would only be by Allah's will, as no one other than Allah had any power. After giving them his guidance, he prayed: "In Him I have put my trust. In Him let the faithful put their trust."(12:67)

وَلَمَّا دَخَلُوا عَلَىٰ يُوسُفَ أَوَىٰ
إِلَيْهِ أَخَاهُ قَالَ إِنِّى أَنَا
أَخُوكَ فَلَا تَبْتَئِسْ بِمَا كَانُوا يَعْمَلُونَ ۰

When they went in to Yusuf,
he embraced his brother, and said:
'I am your brother. Do not grieve
at what they did.'
(12:69)

Again the brothers happily packed their goods and loaded the camels. To the sound of harness bells tinkling and the grunting of animals, they set out once again down the long dusty road to Egypt. This time they were eleven, as Binyamin was along with them. They were now confident that they would be well received in Egypt and would be given all that they wanted.

They all reached Egypt and entered the city in the way their father had advised them. Then they went to the royal store house to buy grain for their family.

When Yusuf عليه السلام saw his younger brother Binyamin, he could hardly hold back his tears of joy. It was more than twenty years since he had seen his brother, who was now in his prime. He greeted all the brothers and took Binyamin aside and embraced him, and confided to

him that he was his lost brother, Yusuf. He comforted him and said he should not grieve over the past doings of their half-brothers. He also told him that he should not let anyone know about this.

While the grain for Binyamin was being weighed out, Yusuf ﷺ put his drinking cup in his younger brother's packs. This was not a trick on the part of the Prophet Yusuf ﷺ, but was done out of great affection for his younger brother. Previously Yusuf ﷺ had done something similar when he put back in his brothers' packs all the money, which they had brought to buy grain. The brothers only realized this when they opened their packs once they were back home. This time too, as a gesture of affection and love to his younger brother, he put his drinking cup in his pack. This was known neither to Binyamin nor to the courtiers.

In the meantime, the measuring cup belonging to the king had been misplaced and the courtiers suspected the brothers of stealing it. As the brothers were passing through the streets of the city, a group of royal guards rushed up to them and shouted: "O you people of the Caravan! Indeed you are thieves!"

They turned back, and asked: "What have you lost?"

"The king's measuring-cup is missing," they replied. "Whoever brings it back shall have a camel-load of corn."

"In God's name," they cried, "you know we did not come to do evil in this land. We are no thieves."

But the guards argued, "What punishment shall be his who stole it, if you prove to be lying?"

The brothers replied, "He in whose pack the cup is found shall be your slave. Thus do we punish the wrongdoers." To this the guards immediately agreed.

In this way the brothers themselves decided the punishment of the guilty, for in this they followed the law of Ibrahim ﷺ. Under the king's law, such a punishment was not possible.

When they opened their packs, there, glinting in the sun, nestled a precious cup. They found the Prophet Yusuf's drinking cup in Binyamin's bag. This was not the cup they were actually looking for, but it was a similar one—a very expensive cup.

This was not a ruse on the part of the Prophet Yusuf ﷺ to prevent his brother from leaving. In the words of the Quran, it was an inspiration, a plan from Allah: "Thus we planned (kidna) for Yusuf." (12:76).

The brothers were terrified when they came to know of the charges of stealing, but they showed no surprise, saying that Binyamin's brother Yusuf had also been a thief. Little did they realize that the king's minister they were addressing was none other than Yusuf عليه السلام himself. Yusuf عليه السلام showed restraint at this gibe and only said, "Your deed was worse. Allah best knows the things you speak of."

قَالُوۡا وَاَقۡبَلُوۡا عَلَيۡهِمۡ مَّاذَا تَفۡقِدُوۡنَ ۞

قَالُوۡا نَفۡقِدُ صُوَاعَ الۡمَلِكِ وَلِمَنۡ جَآءَ بِهٖ حِمۡلُ بَعِيۡرٍ وَّاَنَا بِهٖ زَعِيۡمٌ ۞

They turned back, and asked:
'What have you lost?' 'We miss the king's
drinking-cup,' he replied. 'He that
brings it shall have a camel-load of corn.
I pledge my word for it.'
(12:71-72)

When the courtiers argued with the brothers, over the punishment to be meted out to the thief, they again said that the victim of the theft would be entitled to take the thief as a slave in compensation for the crime committed against him. This was agreed to and Binyamin was kept back by Yusuf عليه السلام.

But soon the brothers worried about their father who had taken a solemn pledge from them to bring back Binyamin. So they pleaded with Yusuf ﷺ to free Binyamin: "Noble prince, this boy has an aged father. Take one of us, instead of him. We can see you are a generous man." One of the brothers offered to remain there as a hostage in place of Binyamin. Legend has it that he was the same brother who had objected to killing Yusuf ﷺ, suggesting that they cast him into a

well instead. But Yusuf ﷺ turned down their request saying: "God forbid that we should take any but the man with whom our propety was found: for then we should be unjust."

Now the brothers were so upset that they did not know what to do. The eldest brother refused to leave Egypt, lacking the courage to show his face to his father. He accused his brothers: "Do you not know that your father took from you a pledge in Allah's name, and that long ago you did your worst with Yusuf? I will not stir from this land until my father gives me leave or Allah makes known to me His judgement." He asked his brothers to return to the old father and tell him: "Father, your son has committed theft. We testify only to what we know. How could we guard against the unforeseen? Inquire at the city where we lodged, and from the caravan with which we travelled. We speak the truth."

When they reached home without Binyamin, they told their ailing father that his son had committed a theft and that the king's minister had kept him as a punishment. The brothers swore to their father that this was the truth, and they even made the people of the caravan bear witness. Their father was absolutely stunned by the story. He knew his darling little Binyamin too well to believe that he had stolen anything. He flatly refused to believe them, thinking that they had plotted to get rid of their youngest brother just as they had plotted against Yusuf ﷺ. So he cried, "No! Your souls have tempted you to evil. But I will have sweet patience (sabr jamil). Allah may bring them all to me... He alone is All-Knowing and Wise."

Yaqub ﷺ pined for his son Yusuf. Ruefully, he thought of how his boyhood dreams had augured his greatness. For himself, the whole world had been plunged into darkness. He had lost his eyesight because of the sheer depth of his grief. If only he could have wept, perhaps his red and swollen eyes might have been able to see again. But they had paled, and then turned white. Everything looked blurred. He had no one with whom to share his sorrow and no one to whom he could complain. So he remained silent. But his faith was still as strong as ever and he observed the discipline of patience—the greatest virtue of the faithful.

The loss of Yusuf ﷺ and Binyamin was so hard for him to bear, yet he poured out his distraction and grief only to Allah. Turning away from his sons, he cried, "How great is my grief for Yusuf!" The sons retorted, "By God! You will never cease to remember Yusuf until you ruin your health or die." But Yaqub ﷺ forgave the sting and malice in the speech of his sons and, like a

قَالَ بَلْ سَوَّلَتْ لَكُمْ أَنْفُسُكُمْ أَمْرًا ۖ
فَصَبْرٌ جَمِيلٌ ۖ عَسَى اللّٰهُ أَنْ يَأْتِيَنِي بِهِمْ جَمِيعًا ۚ
إِنَّهُ هُوَ الْعَلِيمُ الْحَكِيمُ ۝

'No!' cried their father. 'Your souls have tempted you to evil. But I will have sweet patience. Allah may bring them all to me. He alone is all-knowing and wise.'

(12:83)

Prophet of Allah, he still wished them well, and gave sound advice. But he did not lose hope, so he said to his sons:

"O my sons! go and enquire about Yusuf and his brother, and never give up hope of Allah's soothing mercy; truly, no one despairs of Allah's soothing mercy, except those who have no faith."

So the sons of Yaqub ﷺ once again set out for Egypt in the hope that the king's minister would agree to their request and release Binyamin.

Finally the brothers reached Egypt and met Yusuf عليه السلام and pleaded with him to release Binyamin. They told him that their father was an old man who deeply grieved for his son. They went on telling him about the state of health of their father who was heart-broken and had almost lost his eyesight. They also pleaded with Yusuf عليه السلام for charity as they had not brought much money this

time. They all said, "Noble prince, we and our people are scourged with famine." They had spent a great part of their capital and stock-in-trade. "We have brought very little money. Give us some corn, and be charitable to us: Allah rewards the charitable." To their pleadings, Yusuf ﷺ replied: "Do you know what you did to Yusuf and his brother?"

At once the brothers realized that they were in the presence of Yusuf ﷺ!

"What!" the brothers exclaimed.

"Can you indeed be Yusuf?" They could not believe their eyes.

"I am Yusuf," he answered, "and this is my brother. Allah has been very generous to us. Those who keep from evil and endure with fortitude, will not be denied their reward by Allah. They may suffer a great deal, but patience and right conduct are at last rewarded by Allah."

At first, the brothers feared that Yusuf ﷺ might want to punish them, but he treated them kindly. "By the Lord," the brothers said, "Allah has exalted you above us all. We have indeed been guilty." They freely confessed their wrongdoing.

But Yusuf ﷺ was such a kind-hearted person that he did not rebuke them at all and said: "None shall reproach you this day. May Allah forgive you."

Full of amazement and greatly relieved and grateful, the brothers went home.

It is related that the Prophet Muhammad also behaved in exactly the same way as Yusuf ﷸ, when he took hold of the two sides of the gate of the Kabah on the day of the conquest of Makkah and said to the Quraysh: "How do you think I should treat you?" They replied, "We hope for good, you are a noble brother and the son of a noble brother." "I say as my brother Yusuf said," the Prophet replied, "let no one reproach you this day." In this way, the Prophet forgave all his opponents and thus a new chapter was opened in the history of Islam, as all those opponents who in ordinary circumstances would have been beheaded for treachery, ultimately embraced Islam and served its cause—the parallel of which has not been heard of or seen in the entire history of Islam. Such was the power of forgiveness.

Before the brothers left for home, Yusuf ﷸ gave his shirt to them and told them to touch his father's eyes with it, which would restore his sight, and to bring his parents to him. It should be remembered that the brothers had covered up their crime by taking his shirt, putting stains of false blood on it, and pretending that he had been killed by a wolf.

اِذْهَبُوْا بِقَمِيْصِىْ هٰذَا فَاَلْقُوْهُ عَلٰى وَجْهِ اَبِىْ يَاْتِ بَصِيْرًاؕ وَاْتُوْنِىْ بِاَهْلِكُمْ اَجْمَعِيْنَ ۬

Take this shirt of mine and throw it over my father's face: he will recover his sight. Then return to me with all your people.'

(12:93)

While they were on their homeward journey, but still some distance from home, Yaqub ﷺ sensed that they were approaching, because he could smell the scent of Yusuf's shirt. No sooner had the caravan reached their settlement than the father said: "I feel the breath of Yusuf, though you will not believe me." It was as if he felt the presence of Yusuf ﷺ in the air. When a lost-long friend is about to be found or heard of, many people have a sort of foretaste of it, which they call telepathy. In the case of Yaqub ﷺ it was more definite. But the people around Yaqub ﷺ thought he had lost his mind.

"In God's name", said those who heard him, "it is only your old illusion."

As soon as the brothers reached their house, they gave their father the good news that Yusuf ﷺ was alive and as soon as they touched their father's face with his shirt, he regained his sight.

Yaqub ﷺ was overjoyed, and thanking Allah, said, "Did I not tell you, Allah has made known to me what you do not know?"

His sons sank their heads in shame and asked forgiveness of him: "Father, beg for forgiveness for our sins. We have indeed done wrong." He replied, "I shall beg my Lord to forgive you. He is forgiving and merciful." (12:96-98).

The brothers now told their father about how Yusuf ﷺ was now a powerful minister in the lands of Egypt, next only to the king. They also told him about his invitation to them to bring their parents to Egypt. Then, to get ready for the journey, the whole family packed up all their belongings and all their household goods.

They also took along other useful things like tools and weapons, rope and looms. They rolled up their tents and threw them over the backs of their camels. Then they gathered their flocks and herds together and began the slow journey to Egypt, to settle in the land that Yusuf عليه السلام was preparing for them. When they bade farewell to the land of Canaan, little did they know that their people would not come back there for hundreds of years.

To keep up their spirits, they sang as they travelled onwards, and at night they stopped to build fires and bake their bread on hot stones. Then they would sit around the fires, telling the old stories of their tribe. And in the morning they would set off again on the long slow trek. As they moved across the vast expanses of the desert and approached the fertile delta of the Nile, they noticed many changes in the landscape.

Finally, one of the brothers who was ahead of the others called back to them: "Look! There in front of you is the city where our brother Yusuf holds sway! We are almost there!"

They were immediately able to see the rank to which Yusuf عليه السلام had risen. Yusuf عليه السلام embraced his parents and, showing them the deepest respect, made them sit on the throne and said: "Welcome to Egypt, in safety, if Allah wills!" According to an old Egyptian custom, the place of honour at a ceremonial reception is on a seat or a dais, with a special cushion of honour. Seeing the splendour and high position of Yusuf ﷺ, they were awed and all fell prostrate, as a mark of thanksgiving. In this way, the

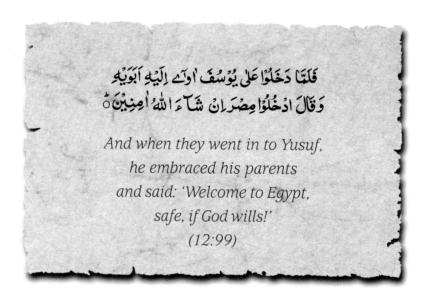

فَلَمَّا دَخَلُوْا عَلٰى يُوْسُفَ اٰوٰۤى اِلَيْهِ اَبَوَيْهِ وَقَالَ ادْخُلُوْا مِصْرَ اِنْ شَاۤءَ اللّٰهُ اٰمِنِيْنَ ۚ

And when they went in to Yusuf,
he embraced his parents
and said: 'Welcome to Egypt,
safe, if God wills!'
(12:99)

dream that Yusuf ﷺ had had as a boy, of the sun, the moon and eleven stars prostrating themselves before him, had at last come true.

"This", Yusuf ﷺ reminded his father, "is the meaning of my dream which my Lord has fulfilled." He explained that his parents were the sun and the moon, and his brothers were the stars!

Overwhelmed with gratitude to Allah for delivering him from prison, for reuniting him with his parents and for guiding his brothers back to the right path, Yusuf ﷺ prostrated himself before Allah saying: "O my Lord! You have indeed bestowed on me power, and taught me the